MW00635721

A Promise

A Vow of Love for Baby
and a Message of Hope for Mom

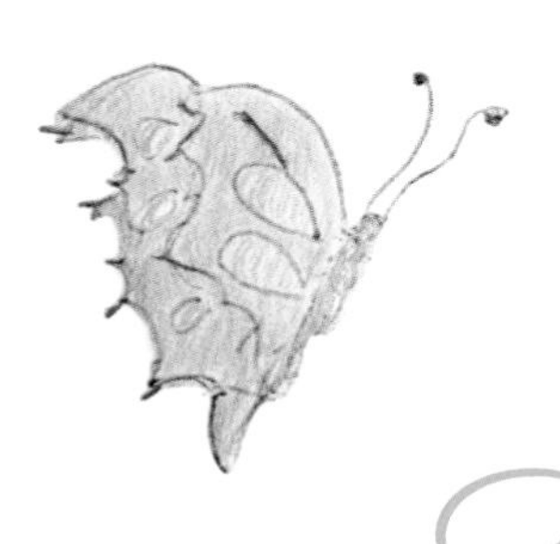

A Promise

A Vow of Love for Baby and a Message of Hope for Mom

Dr. Annie Rohr

ISBN 978-1-948011-39-6

Legacy Isle Publishing
1000 Bishop St., Ste. 806
Honolulu, HI 96813
www.legacyislepublishing.net
info@legacyislepublishing.net

Printed in Korea

This book is dedicated to my sweet little girl.
I want to thank you for the honor of being your mom.
It is a blessing to see you grow and I am proud to be on this journey with you. I pray you will be proud of me and our journey too.
Love you, my little family.

Introduction

This book is for all mothers and babies. It was written to celebrate moms who may be on a different journey from "everyone else." It is for new moms—or any mom who needs support. It is to remind us that no matter what phase we are in as a mom, we are going to get through it and be okay.

This book is a promise of love to babies and a message of hope for moms. In part, it is the voice of a mother to her child, but the words are also there for Mom to hear a gentle and comforting encouragement. It was written and also mostly Illustrated by me, a "not-so-perfect" mama and psychologist on her own journey. This is not a perfect book with perfect pictures. It was—and is—my reality. I hope it helps you. Please remember, things don't have to be perfect to be beautiful.

My intent was for you to read this promise of love to your little ones—and to take in the little messages and reminders at the bottom of each page meant for you, Mama, to help you through your journey.

Throughout the book, I have hidden little hearts for love and butterflies (a symbol of change and hope) to represent the changes of becoming a mom. Each butterfly was drawn by a mom who has helped me along my journey. Some of these moms also had difficulty postpartum and were there for me, with great advice, amazing help and supportive words. Notice how each butterfly is different. This represents how each mom is a different butterfly and each journey is unique. We cannot compare ourselves to each other. Rather, we have to embrace our differences and provide support to one another.

—Dr. Annie Rohr

Hello, my little angel.
I know in my heart and my soul that
I am blessed to have you.

I truly thought this would feel different, more natural.
I'm not sure I am good enough,
I definitely do not have all the answers.
I thought we would feel connected
right from the start and
I would just know what do.

For Mama: You are not alone. Many women have similar feelings. For most of us, we do not know what we are doing and we don't feel like we thought we would. Deep breath, Mama, you will be okay and you'll get through this.

But here we are, my little one.
Turns out, we have a different path to take
than I imagined.

I have to figure you out a bit.
I understand that you have
a whole new world to adjust to.
And it turns out, so do I.
My whole world shifted the minute you were born.

Mama, your life has changed and it is okay that you need to take time to adjust to it. You are both doing a lot of new things! Please give yourself a break. Step outside if you can and get some fresh air, or take a short, gentle walk. It helps to do this once a day or more. Take a moment for you.

I do not feel like myself. I miss my old self.
I miss me. I miss my time.
I'm not sure how to be me and be your mom just yet.
And I look at you and I know
you deserve someone who loves you,
someone who knows what you need.
I need to take a deep breath and accept that it's okay.
I will figure this out.

Take a deep breath, Mama. It is okay to miss or grieve for your life before the baby. It is natural to miss it. Talk to someone if you need to. It may be helpful to start a journal and write when you can. It can help you process feelings and it can be an amazing gift later to go back and read through your feelings and changes. Having a baby is a huge life change and it takes time to find your way and adjust.

I promise you, my little baby, that I will get there.
I promise you that we will adjust to one another
and every day we will figure each other out
more and more.
Some days I will feel lost.
But I assure you, I will keep you safe.
I will also do what it takes to keep me
healthy and safe so I may be there for you.
I'll take deep breaths when I need to.
I'll remind myself that we are okay too.

Deep breath again, Mama. You have to take care of yourself too. Please take moments for yourself. Make sure you are resting and eating when you can. It's okay to ask for help when you need it. You are not alone. Talk to a friend, another mom, a therapist; consider seeking out a postpartum doula for extra help if you need to.

Some moms and babies figure it out from the start...
but most have a little journey to take.
I ask that you be patient with me, my sweetheart.

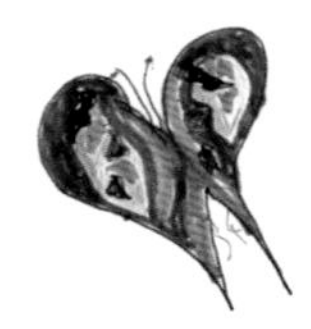

Focus on a single moment that felt good or is characteristic of baby that makes you smile in a difficult time. Think of the soft skin, little feet...just a thought to focus on to get you through a hard moment. Tell yourself, "This is a tough moment, it's okay to have tough moments. It will pass. I am not alone."

I am still learning your cries,
I am still adjusting to not sleeping,
I'm still finding my feet as a mom.
It's sort of like being a butterfly.
I'm still the caterpillar in the cocoon.
I'm learning and growing
and soon I'll emerge as a butterfly mom.

Mama, you are so tired. This is a phase that will pass. Get rest when you can and know you are loved. This is the hard part. It's survival, and it will pass. Picture yourself as a butterfly that has just emerged. You are just beginning to move your wings and getting used to this new body. It takes time...but, soon, you'll fly.

You see, we are both in new worlds.

I promise you that each day,
I'll get better and stronger.
I promise you, we will connect soon.
I promise you that one day,
I'll know exactly what you need.
We will have so many fun and lovely moments.
We will dance to our own tune.

Take time out to breathe or count to ten. Remember a song that makes you happy—sing it or think of the words. Even dance or sway a little. Anything helps. Tell yourself, "This moment will pass and you will get through."

But for now little one,
let's agree that our journey will be ours...unique.
For now, I will struggle sometimes,
I may feel confused, a little lost...
but I am here for you.

I will find ways to make us happy.
We will have a story just for us.
Sometimes the hardest starts have beautiful stories.

Know that every mom-and-baby duo is different. Try not to compare yourself to others. You and your baby will create your own way that is right for both of you. You will discover how to sleep with baby, comfort baby, feed baby. And it may differ from your friends, and that is okay. It is what is best for you both. And only the two of you will know what works!

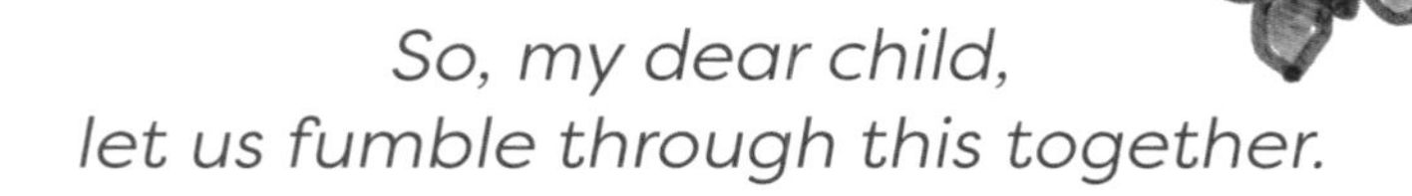

So, my dear child,
let us fumble through this together.

Mama will need to take deep breaths and moments
to accept all these changes.
I did not just step into the role of Mama,
I have to learn and practice and it’s okay.
I promise you, I will figure you out,
I will find my place.
You have nothing to worry about.

Take a deep breath, Mama. Close your eyes for a moment and breathe in a feeling of warmth and calm. It is easy to focus on the hard parts, where we fumble. Instead, try and think of something that went well. Think about the one thing that you got through or did well. You got this, Mama, one moment at a time.

loved
BEYOND MEASURE

Very soon, we will have silly talks, songs to sing,
inside jokes, and so many adventures.
We will play at the beach, we will eat treats together,
we will take walks. I will show you all the flowers.

Every day will be different.
We have to remember:
Some moments will be amazing, some just okay,
and others will be hard throughout our lives together.

No matter your age,
sometimes I'll know just what to do and other times,
I'll have no clue. That's the reality of being a mom.
No matter the moment, we will get through it.
I will keep you safe and you will feel loved.

Mama, time will heal this. Please remember that every "very hard part" is just a phase that will pass. The crying, the teething, the fears—it is just a moment. And another moment will come along soon.

KEEP GATE
CLOSED

This hard part will pass sooner than we know.
Time, acceptance, patience
and asking for help if we need it
will get us through.

I will do my best and notice you
in this moment, as you are.
Precious.
Because I know some day,
I'll miss even the hard parts.

Gratitude can often bring good feelings, so take a breath and a moment to think of something—or someone—you feel grateful to have in your life. Appreciate the moment and celebrate yourself for your latest accomplishment, big or small.

Trust me, my angel,
I will be the best mom I can be from now till forever.
We just have some bumps to adjust to.

I look forward to the day when I cannot remember
my life without you.

I just need some time to get there.

Let's grow together, my baby.
Let's create our story.

Some thoughts for you, Mama

Use the words that feel right or healing to you and create a mantra. A mantra is a set of words that you will say again and again in moments when you need to feel better, to comfort you. You are important and will get through this. Your journey will be different from anyone else's and that will be okay.

Mantra words for Mom:

I am going to be okay. I am not alone.
It will not always feel hard. It will get better.
There will be good moments too.
Some moments will be amazing.

Time will heal the hard parts.
The hardest parts are passing phases.
I need to take care of myself.
I need to ask for help when I need it.
I need to get rest when I can.
I need to look for good moments too.

In the hard moments, tell yourself:

This is a hard moment. Many parents out there have these.
I am not alone. I am going to be kind to myself.

Take a deep breath. This moment will pass.

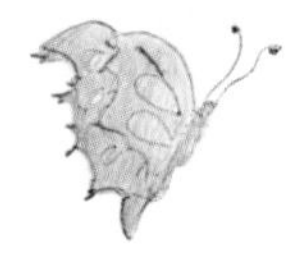

Some gentle reminders and suggestions:

Don't forget to notice the good moments.

Fresh air and movement are beneficial—getting your body moving (even just a little) helps a lot.

Making connections with people and talking helps. It's okay to ask *for help.*

Start a grateful journal or jar.

At least once a day, write down a moment that went well or you are grateful for in your journal, or place it in a jar where you can see it. In hard times, review these good moments.

When do I know it's time to seek help?

It is best to seek support at any time you feel you need to on your journey. *Any time* is the right time! There is support out there, even if you are not sure you need it. Best to check, ask and find out! Any support or helpful connection is good! You do not have to wait till things feel worse. You can connect or reach out at any time to ask about how you feel or find support. If you feel unable to care for yourself or your child; feel your thoughts are getting in the way of caring for your baby or self; or feel helpless, hopeless or have had thoughts of suicide, please seek help immediately.

Talk to Your Doctor

Ask for help and resources even if you are not sure you need them. Better to have them than not have them.

Postpartum Support International

The most comprehensive resource. You can get help directly, access support call or text lines, online groups, training and more.

www.postpartum.net
Phone Helpline (English and Spanish): 1-800-944-4773
Text Helpline: 1-503-894-9453

Mental Health Providers

You can ask your doctor for a referral, find one on the Postpartum International directory or look up a provider on a psychologist or therapy search engine such as psychologytoday.com (look for perinatal mental health providers in your area). Please know many offer online visits or home visits to accommodate you!

Postpartum Doulas

They are amazing in providing help and support for you and baby.

Grow Your Community

Consider joining a mom group or seek out a mom friend in your area. Search online for mom or family groups or ways to meet other moms in your area. There are many programs, forums and even apps out there to connect moms and families.

Acknowledgments

Love and thanks to my very supportive husband.
Thank you for accepting me and my changes. Thank you for
loving me as I am even during the very rough parts.
You are a wonderful friend and, now, father. I am blessed. And
thank you so much for your help with the illustrations
and colors. I know it was not easy sometimes.

Special thanks to all the moms out there who became a part
of my life, my team. Thank you for the support, guidance
and love. You are butterflies.

About the Author

My name is Dr. Annie Rohr. I am a clinical psychologist and marriage and family therapist in Honolulu, Hawaii. I am also the author of *Finding the Warm and Fuzzies*, a children's book designed to help kids manage their emotions. In my career as a therapist, I seek to help people discover the best versions of themselves. I want to remind everyone about how to create happiness and enjoy moments while learning from hard times.

Becoming a mother to a little girl is a recent step on my own journey. This little blessing brought a lot of new emotions and quite an adventure. I found myself struggling a lot with conflicting feelings and postpartum anxiety. *How could a therapist not know how to handle all of this?* I had all the tools, and yet felt lost, isolated and alone.

To me, motherhood felt like becoming a butterfly. It really felt like a major change was happening. I was emerging as something new. I found that there were things I wish I had known, things I wish I could have told myself, or someone else had shared with me. I found I didn't relate to a lot of the books out there or what other parents said they went through. My experiences were different; they felt harder than what people talked about. So I created this book for me and for others who needed to hear these messages, to say that we are not alone, although our journey is unique, and that is okay.

www.drannierohr.com